The Bandstand

Dan Newell

NEW JUICE PUBLISHING

At the edge of a town there is a hill.

And on the top of the hill there is an old wooden hut.

You might think it would be a bit lonely living up there,
all alone, in a hut, on the top of a hill.

You might think it would be a bit quiet living
up there, all alone, in a hut, on the top of a hill.

In fact, if you look inside that lonely old hut
on the top of the hill you will find...

Billy's Band.

What a wonderful sound they're making!

They love coming here to the hut on the hill where they can practise as loud as they like without disturbing the town.

That's Billy standing at the front, waving his arms around.

He's the conductor. The finest and wisest and most whiskery conductor that ever lived. He makes sure everyone is playing the right notes in the right order at the right time. He always looks smart and he loves music more than you love sweets.

Nobody knows how old he is.

He could be a hundred.

He could be a thousand.

No, that's silly.

But it feels like Billy's been here forever, making music for us all.

The band are having a final practice before their big performance at the summer fair in front of the whole town.

It's time to get on the shiny red bus and go to the concert.

Billy takes the register to make sure everyone is here.

They all look very smart in their concert clothes don't they?

They all look very excited.

There's Valerie the violinist, a rather serious young girl,

And Chelsea the cellist, one of the best in the world.

Here's Tom the trumpet player, who tends to show off a bit,

And Tina the trombonist, who's always giggling in fits.

Next it's Toby with his tuba, he's so thoughtful and mild,

And Danny the drummer, whose rhythms drive you wild.

There's Clarissa with her clarinet, the cleverest member of the band,

And Sam the saxophonist, the most relaxed guy in the land.

Then last but not least at the back of the queue,

Holding her bright and shiny flute,

It's... Jane.

Jane the flute player?

That doesn't sound right, does it?

Billy has a rule that everyone in the band must choose a stage name which matches their instrument, but today is Jane's first ever performance with Billy's Band and she's so nervous she hasn't been able to think about her stage name.

Look how worried she is.

Her tummy is so tumbly and her fingers so fumbly, she's worried she won't be able to play at all.

Billy understands. He remembers his first ever performance when he was so nervous he snapped his conductor's stick in half.

'My dear Jane,' Billy shouts from the front of the bus.

'Fret not about your name. Focus only on your breathing and have faith in yourself!'

Billy always knows the right thing to say.

The whole town is having a wonderful time
in the park.

There's Mrs Poodle with her dogs.
They look a bit naughty don't they?

There's Mr Cool in his ice cream van.
He looks a bit chilly doesn't he?

And there's Billy's Band setting up
their instruments in the bandstand.

There's already a big crowd gathering,
waiting for the concert to begin.

It's time for the performance to start.

Billy taps his stick on the music stand.

He raises his arms in the air.

And the band begins to play.

Danny's drums beat a lively march while
Tom, Tina and Toby lead the brassy tune.

But Billy is not happy. He knows it doesn't sound quite right and conductors always notice if it doesn't sound right.

Jane is playing her flute so quietly she can barely be heard.

And she's not concentrating on the music or watching Billy conducting like she ought to be.

She can't stop gawping at the sprawling mass of people who all seem to be gawping back at her.

Her eyes are big and bulging and brimming with tears.

Billy knows what to do.

He bends towards Jane to get her attention.

He points at her eyes and then at his own,
a reminder that she should only look at him.

It works.

By keeping her eyes on Billy (and not on the big audience)
Jane begins to relax and trill the most beautiful notes
on her flute.

Billy's whiskery smile spreads across his jolly face and Jane can hardly believe how well she is suddenly playing.

The audience are all smiling and tapping their feet.

The band are playing the best they've ever played.

Everyone is so happy.

It's such a joyful scene.

Oh no.

It's exactly the kind of joyful scene in a story where you know something is about to go horribly wrong...

Across the park, Mrs Poodle is trying to listen to the band, but she can't keep control of her naughty dogs.

Look at them whining and yapping and pulling on their leads.

What on earth is wrong with them?

They've been behaving especially badly ever since the band began to play.

Oh no!

The dogs have escaped and charged onto the stage!

The band tries to carry on playing but it's impossible. Valerie
has lost her bow and they've even knocked Billy onto the floor!

As he struggles to his feet and watches the mayhem, Billy
has a brilliant idea.

'Jane!' he calls. 'It's your flute!'

'My flute?' she replies. 'What do you mean Billy?'

'The dogs are driven mad by your wonderful high notes!
There's only one thing for it!'

Without Billy needing to say another word, Jane
understands what she has to do.

Without a flicker of fear, Jane raises the flute to her mouth, takes a deep breath and begins to play.

Look how the dogs are drawn to her high notes!

They howl and circle around her feet.

Like the pied piper, Jane leads the dogs away
from the stage with her beautiful strong solo,
and back to a rather red-faced Mrs Poodle
who immediately takes them home.

Everybody cheers.

'Well done my dear Jane!' says Billy.
'I knew you could do it.'

Beaming with pride she replies,
'Actually Billy, you can call me Faith'.

'Faith?' asks Billy.

'Well, like you said, I just needed
to have faith in myself!'

The band strike up another tune and
the audience bursts into applause.

And there she is, Faith the flute player,
a proper member of Billy's Band at last.

Now you have met Billy and his amazing band...

Valerie
Violin

Chelsea
Cello

Tom
Trumpet

Tina
Trombone

Toby
Tuba

Danny
Drums

Clarissa
Clarinet

Sam
Saxophone

Faith
Flute

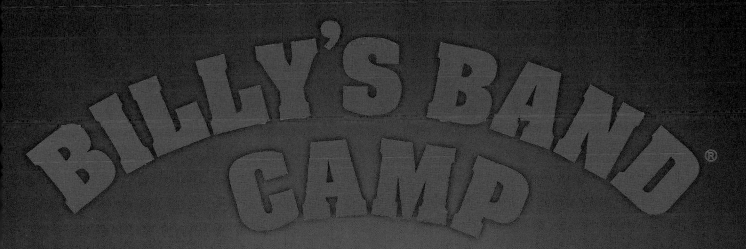

Welcome to Billy's Band Camp.

It's time for you to join in with Billy as he guides you through the musical activities on the CD.

Listen to the CD. Billy will conduct the band – and he has some questions for you.

Track 1

Billy's Band theme tune
Listen to the song. Learn the words and sing along.

Track 2

Introduction
The band is warming up. Try to identify the different instruments. Be quick, as you only have 7 seconds!

Track 3

Faith plays Badinerie by Bach
What is the **pitch** of this song – is it high or low?
What is the **tempo** of this song – is it fast or slow?

Track 4

Billy talks to Faith
Faith tells us the answers to the questions in track 3. There is a guest appearance from Toby the tuba player. The tuba is the lowest pitched member of the brass family. Can you name three other instruments in the brass family?

Track 5

Faith plays an excerpt from Syrinx by Debussy
How does this piece compare to Badinerie, on track 3? Think about the **tempo**, **pitch** and **mood** of the music – whether it's happy, sad, mysterious…

Track 6

Call and response game
Billy introduces us to call and response, telling us how to play this game. It's pretty simple, he'll clap you a **rhythm** and you just clap it back!

Another chance to play call and response

Billy will clap you a **rhythm** and you have to clap it back. Remember not to get faster as the **tempo** must stay the same. Try being Billy and compose your own **rhythms** to clap – see if anyone will copy you!

Now Tom plays a trumpet solo. Just sit back and listen.

Call and response using sounds

Try to copy the sounds Billy is making. It is important to listen to the **duration** of each sound as some are long, some short and some medium. Did you know that note durations can be combined to make up different rhythms?

Billy will then use **dynamics**, so try to copy the Italian words Billy uses making sure you say them at the correct **dynamic** (volume). Turn the page to find out what the Italian words mean.

Build a song

Billy shows us the main ingredients of a song. Listen to how the **texture** builds, starting off thinly with only one instrument and getting thicker as lots of instruments join in.

Listen to the **timbre** of Tom's trumpet. How do you think the sound differs from the solo he played earlier, on track 7?

Learning to improvise

Billy, Faith and Tina start improvising. When it's your turn, you can play anything you like – but only use the notes marked with dots on the keyboard below – C, D, E, G and A.

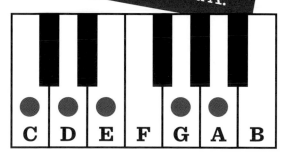

C D E F G A B

Track 11

Improvise
This whole track is dedicated for you to improvise along with Billy's Band! Try singing, playing your instrument if you have one or beating rhythmns. If you don't have an instrument, why not make your own instrument noises! Try playing different note **durations**, **rhythms** and **dynamics** but remember – always keep the **tempo** steady.

Track 12

Farewell from Billy
Stay in touch with Billy's Band and learn more about music on Billy's website, **billysband.co.uk**

Musical words

Duration
The length of a note or rest, from short to long

Dynamics
The volume of the music, from quiet to loud:
Pianissimo – very quiet
Piano – quiet
Mezzoforte – moderately loud
Forte – loud
Fortissimo – very loud

Improvisation
Making up your own tune as you go along

Mood
How the music makes you feel

Note
A symbol which indicates the **duration** and **pitch** of a sound

Pitch
How high or low a note sounds

Rest
A symbol which indicates an interval of silence

Rhythm
Different durations of **notes** and **rests** put together create a rhythm

Solo
A piece of music performed by one person

Tempo
The speed of the music, from fast to slow

Texture
The amount of instruments performing at the same time creates the texture, from thin (few instruments) to thick (lots of instruments)

Timbre
The different sounds an instrument can make

Answers to the questions Billy asks on the CD Track 3: The **pitch** is high, the **tempo** is fast. **Track 4:** As well as the **tuba**, the **trumpet**, **trombone** and **French horn** are all members of the brass family. **Track 5:** The **tempo** is slow, the **pitch** is high, the **mood** is sad and mysterious. **Track 9:** Tom is using a **mute**. It fits into the end of his trumpet and changes the **timbre** and **volume**.